Slide In

Advisory Panel

Cathy Bogusat
Christine Finochio
Mary Francone
Helen Hohmann
Jan McDonald
John McLaughlin
Sharon McPhail
Fiona Morrison
Mary Nall
Lorraine Prokopchuk

Senior Program Consultant

Jennette MacKenzie

Senior Consultants

Sharon Siamon
Frieda Wishinsky

I(T)P Nelson

an International Thomson Publishing company

Toronto • Albany • Bonn • Boston • Cincinnati • Detroit • London • Madrid • Melbourne
Mexico City • New York • Pacific Grove • Paris • San Francisco • Singapore • Tokyo • Washington

I(T)P® International Thomson Publishing

The ITP logo is a trademark under licence
www.thomson.com

© Copyright ITP®Nelson, 1999

Published by
I(T)P® Nelson

A division of Thomson Canada Limited
1120 Birchmount Road
Scarborough, Ontario M1K 5G4
www.nelson.com

Printed and bound in Canada
5 6 7 8 9 0/ML/7 6 5 4 3 2 1

Canadian Cataloguing in Publication Data
Main entry under title:
Nelson language arts, [levels A-E]
For use in kindergarten and grade 1.
Contents: Level A. Jump in — Level B. Swing in — Level C. Slide in — Level D. Zoom in — Level E. Dive in.
ISBN 0-17-618544-5 (level A)   ISBN 0-17-618545-3 (level B)
ISBN 0-17-618546-1 (level C)   ISBN 0-17-618547-X (level D)
ISBN 0-17-618548-8 (level E)

1. Readers (Primary). I. Siamon, Sharon. II. Wishinsky, Frieda

PE1119.N44 1998   428.6   C98-930370-5

Publisher: Mark Cobham
Executive Editor: Susan Green
Production Coordinator: Theresa Thomas
Marketing Manager: Mark Cressman
Art Direction and Design: Sylvia Vander Schee and Peggy Rhodes
Cover Illustration: Jenny Campbell

Table of Contents

Good Night

by Penelope Coad

This little fish sleeps
in the sea.

This little bird sleeps
in a tree.

This little horse sleeps
on his legs.

This little hen sleeps
on her eggs.

This little pig sleeps
in a pen.

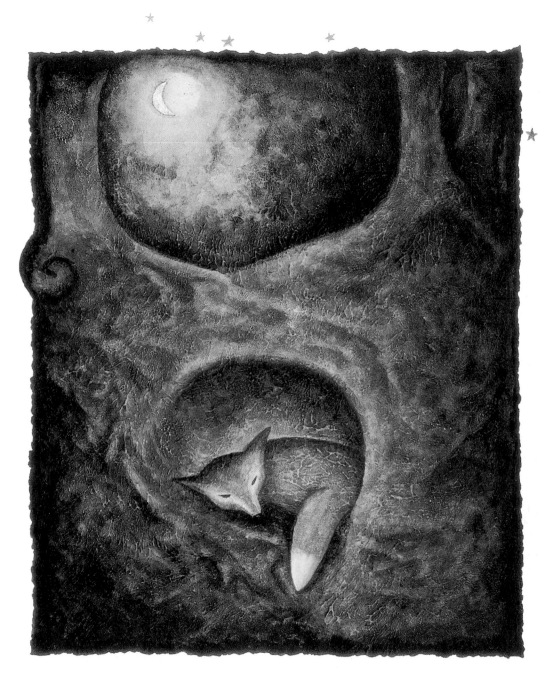

This little fox sleeps
in a den.

This little lamb sleeps
by the door.

This little dog sleeps
on the floor.

This little bat sleeps
overhead.

And me?

I sleep in my own little bed.

Good night.

Boots

by Susan Green

Ben had new red boots.
He put them on the wrong feet.

"You can't go out like that," said Sarah.
"You look funny."

"Come here. Let me help you."
Sarah put dots inside the boots.

"See the dots?" asked Sarah.
"They show you left and right."

Ben put his boots on again.
"Now put on your mitts," said Sarah.

Ben put his mitts on the wrong hands.
"Ben! Ben! Not again!" said Sarah.

Which Is Which?

by Karen Magnuson Beil

Left hand, right hand.
How can you tell?

Look very closely—
The left has an **L**.

But Granny Did!

by Margaret Wild

Simon and Susie took Granny to the fair.

Simon and Susie didn't want
to ride on the roller coaster ...

but Granny did!

Simon and Susie didn't want
to pat the pig ...

but Granny did!

Simon and Susie didn't want
to have their faces painted ...

but Granny did!

Granny didn't want to go home ...

but Simon and Susie did!

What Bugs Do

by Susan Green

This is a caterpillar.
A caterpillar crawls.
It eats leaves.

This is a dragonfly.
A dragonfly sees all around.
It has very big eyes.

This is a grasshopper.
A grasshopper hops.
It has long legs.

This is an ant.
An ant carries food.
It is very strong.

This is a bee.
A bee buzzes.
It makes honey.

This is a butterfly.
A butterfly flies.
It has big wings.

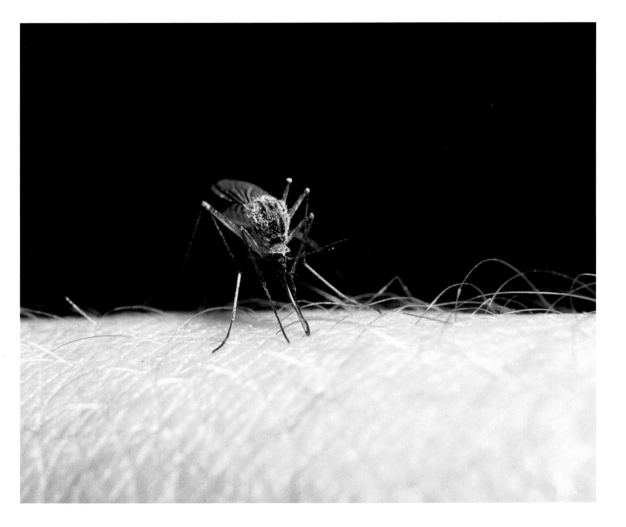

This is a mosquito.
A mosquito bites.
Ouch!

Just Watch

by Myra Cohn Livingston

Watch how far I'm jumping.

Watch how far I hop.

Watch how long I'm skipping.

Watch how fast I stop.

Our New Car

by Frieda Wishinsky

Mom's buying a new car.
I hope it's big and red.
I hope it goes fast.

Here comes Mom in the new car.

The new car isn't big.
It's small.

The new car isn't red.
It's yellow.

I get into the new car and
sit beside Mom.
I put on my seat belt.

The car smells new and
the seat feels smooth.

The horn sounds loud.

"Let's go for a ride."
We like our new car!

Feed Speedy

by Sharon Siamon

Jean came home.
She saw a note on the table.

"Here, Speedy," Jean said.
"Eat your food."

Pete came home.
He saw the note, too.

"Here, Speedy," said Pete.
"Eat your food."

Dad came home.
He saw the note on the table.

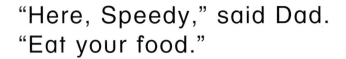

"Here, Speedy," said Dad.
"Eat your food."

Mom came home.
"Did anyone feed Speedy?" she called.

"I did!" shouted Pete.
"I did!" shouted Jean.
"I did!" shouted Dad.

"Speedy, you are a greedy dog."

Make a Puppet

by Frieda Wishinsky

Get a paper bag.

Get some paper, markers, scissors,
and glue.

Make two eyes.
Glue them on the top of the bag.

Make a red tongue.
Glue it under the flap.

Make two big ears.
Glue the ears on the sides of the bag.

Put your hand inside the bag.
Make your dog bark.

Acknowledgments

"Good Night" text copyright © Penelope Coad, 1994, illustrations copyright © Dominique Falla, 1994. Published by Nelson Australia Pty Ltd in 1994. Reprinted with permission. "Which Is Which?" by Karen Magnuson Beil. Reprinted by permission of LADYBUG Magazine, May 1997, Vol. 7, No. 9 © 1997 by Karen Magnuson Beil. "But Granny Did!" text copyright © Margaret Wild, 1994, illustrations copyright © Ian Forss, 1994. Published by Nelson Australia Pty Ltd in 1994. Reprinted with permission. "Just Watch" by Myra Cohn Livingston, copyright renewed 1986, reprinted by permission of Marian Reiner. "Our New Car" and "Make a Puppet" copyright © Frieda Wishinsky, 1998. "Feed Speedy" copyright © Sharon Siamon, 1998.

Illustrations

Dominique Falla, pp.4-15; Per Gurth, pp.16-21, 24-34; Jenny Campbell, pp.42-43; Scot Ritchie, pp.44-49; Sean Dawdy, pp.50-57; Toni Goffe, pp.58-63.

Photographs

Leroy Simon/Visuals Unlimited, p.35, 39; © Corel Corporation, p.36; William J. Weber/Visuals Unlimited, p.37; Paul McCormick/The Image Bank, p.38; Maslowski/Visuals Unlimited, p.40; R. Gunter/First Light, p.41.